STOCKING STUMPERS

CHRISTMAS 2005
GOLF EDITION

**By S. Claus
with help from Jack Kreismer**

Red-Letter Press, Inc.

STOCKING STUMPERS: GOLF - Christmas 2005 Edition
Copyright ©2005 Red-Letter Press, Inc.
ISBN-13: 978-0-940462-27-4
ISBN-10: 0-940462-27-3
Printed in the United States of America

For information:

Red-Letter Press, Inc.
P.O. Box 393, Saddle River, NJ 07458
www.Red-LetterPress.com

Acknowledgments

A Stocking Stumpers salute to Santa's "subordinate clauses":

Cover design and typography: **s.w.artz, inc.**

Santa illustration: **Jack Kreismer, Sr.**

Others: **Tom Lehmann, Doug Dragon, Jr.**

Jeff Kreismer, Bryan Leach

A personal message from Santa

'Twas the night before Christmas
and I left the North Pole
to bring to your stocking
a fresh lump of coal;
But St. Nick's got heart
and your sins weren't voluminous,
so I brought you a gift
in lieu of bituminous;
Now since you've escaped
my long list of lumpers,
I've left you instead
Santa's favorite, *Stocking Stumpers*.

Merry Christmas!

S. Claus

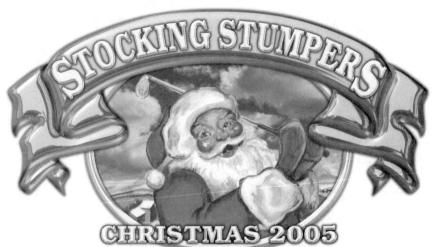

STOCKING STUMPERS

CHRISTMAS 2005
GOLF EDITION

FIRST THINGS FIRST

1. What is Tiger Woods' first name?
2. In 1979 who became the first player known to score lower than his age, shooting a 67 at the Quad Cities Open at the age of 66?
3. What woman comes first on the World Golf Hall of Fame alphabetical list?
4. Who was the first African American to play at the Masters?
5. Who was the first player to win $100,000 in a year? (Hint: The year was 1963.)

ANSWERS

1. Eldrick.
2. Sam Snead.
3. Amy Alcott.
4. Lee Elder, in 1975.
5. Arnold Palmer, $128,230 in 1963.

WHAT'S IN A NAME?

1. What is the real first name of Chi Chi Rodriguez?
2. The "National Invitation Tournament" is the original name of what golf tournament?
3. "Big Mama" is the nickname of what golfer?
4. What nickname did Bobby Jones give his putter?
5. What famed golfer was known as "The Hawk?"

ANSWERS

1. Juan.
2. The Masters.
3. JoAnne Carner.
4. Calamity Jane.
5. Ben Hogan.

CHIP SHOT

"Golfers find it a very trying matter to turn at the waist,
particularly if they have a lot of waist to turn."

-*Harry Vardon*

ARNIE

1. In what year did Arnold Palmer compete in his last Masters Tournament?
2. When did he win his first Masters?
3. In what Pennsylvania town was Palmer born?
4. Palmer served three years in which branch of the military?
5. What college did he attend?

ANSWERS

1. 2004.
2. In 1958. (He went on to win three more—in 1960, 1962 and 1964.)
3. Latrobe, in 1929.
4. The Coast Guard.
5. Wake Forest.

A ROUND OF GOLF

Play the eighteen holes below by unscrambling
the words listed and then placing them in the proper spaces
to complete the following: "If you pick up a golfer
and hold him or her close to your ear, like a shell, ..."

OYU   LIWL   RAHE   NA   BIALI

＿ ＿ ＿   ＿ ＿ ＿ ＿   ＿ ＿ ＿ ＿

＿ ＿   ＿ ＿ ＿ ＿

ANSWER

You will hear an alibi.

CHIP SHOT

"Golf is a game where the ball always lies poorly
and the player always lies well."

-Mike Ryan

MASTERFUL

1. Who did Tiger Woods beat in a playoff to win the 2005 Masters?
2. Who has won the most Masters?
3. What was introduced at the 1949 Masters?
4. "One Magical Sunday" is a book about what Masters winner?
5. Who was the first man to win the Masters three times?

ANSWERS

1. Chris DiMarco.
2. Jack Nicklaus, 6.
3. The green jacket. (Sam Snead was the first recipient.)
4. Phil Mickelson, the green jacket winner in 2004.
5. Jimmy Demaret.

FACT OR FIB?

1. It is legal to use a pool cue as a putter.
2. A Senior Tour player must be at least 60 years old.
3. The founder of the Walker Cup in 1922 is President George W. Bush's great grandfather.
4. In order for a ball overhanging the cup to be considered a made putt it must fall within five seconds.
5. Richard Burton competed in and won the British Open.

ANSWERS

1. Fib- It was banned in an 1895 ruling.
2. Fib- The minimum age is 50.
3. Fact.
4. Fib- Ten seconds are allowed.
5. Fact- He won in 1939. Of course, it wasn't the Richard Burton who married Elizabeth Taylor.

QUOTE, UNQUOTE

Who said it? ... And about whom?

1. "They always used to say the wind stopped for Hogan. Now it stops for (him)."
2. "He's the biggest crowd pleaser since the invention of the portable sanitary facility."
3. "When he plays well, he wins. When he plays badly, he finishes second. When he plays terrible, he finishes third."
4. "My Sunday best is a Wednesday afternoon compared to him."
5. "There are 326 golf courses in the greater Palm Springs area, and he never knows which one he's playing until after he's teed off."

ANSWERS

1. Jack Nicklaus, on Tiger Woods.
2. Bob Hope, on Arnold Palmer.
3. Johnny Miller, on Jack Nicklaus.
4. Nick Faldo, on John Daly.
5. Bob Hope, on former president Gerald Ford.

POLITICALLY CORRECT

1. What former president made a hole in one on Labor Day 1961, at the Bel Air Country Club in Los Angeles?

2. During the 1960 campaign John F. Kennedy referred to what outgoing president as the "Duffer-in-Chief" because he played the game so often?

3. "I deny allegations by Bob Hope that during my last game, I hit an eagle, a birdie, an elk, and a moose." Who said it?

4. What '90s chief executive said this? "The problem with golf is that I have to deal with a humiliation factor."

5. Former president Bill Clinton is an avid golfer who shares a common trait with Ronald Reagan and George Bush senior. What is it?

ANSWERS

1. Richard M. Nixon.
2. Dwight D. Eisenhower.
3. Gerald R. Ford.
4. George Bush.
5. They're left-handed.

CHIP SHOT

"The devoted golfer is an anguished soul who has learned a lot about putting just as an avalanche victim has learned a lot about snow."

-Dan Jenkins

LINK THE LINKS

Match the course with the country in which it's located.

1. Falsterbo	a. Canada
2. Royal Melbourne	b. Republic of Ireland
3. Gleneagles	c. Northern Island
4. Banff Springs	d. Japan
5. Castelconturbia	e. Australia
6. Ballybunion	f. United States
7. Chantilly	g. Sweden
8. Harbour Town Links	h. Scotland
9. Fujioka	i. Italy
10. Royal County Down	j. France

ANSWERS

1. g
2. e
3. h
4. a
5. i
6. b
7. j
8. f
9. d
10. c

POTPOURRI

1. Who's the only woman to win the U.S. Open at Wimbledon in tennis and to play on the LPGA Tour?
2. As a teenager, Paul Azinger caddied for what LPGA great?
3. Name the only golfer to win consecutive British Open titles in the '80s.
4. What is the depth of a golf hole?
5. This man was a two-sport star at the University of Colorado, 1967 NCAA champion in golf and a two-time All-Big Eight selection as a football defensive back. Can you name him?

ANSWERS

1. Althea Gibson, who won tennis' U.S. Open in 1957, Wimbledon in 1958 and played on the LPGA Tour from 1964 to 1969.
2. Mickey Wright.
3. Tom Watson, in 1982 and 1983.
4. 4".
5. Hale Irwin.

HOLIDAY HO HO HOS

It's time for a stumpers break. See if you can answer these groaners from Santa's social director, Henny Elfman.

1. What's it called when you purchase a set of clubs at list price?
2. How can you tell the golfers in church?
3. What do hackers and condemned playgrounds have in common?
4. What are the four worst words you could hear during a round of golf?
5. What type of engine do they use in golf carts?

ANSWERS

1. Getting shafted.
2. They're the ones who pray with the interlocking grip.
3. Lousy swings.
4. "It's still your turn!"
5. Fore cylinder.

A SIMPLE YES OR NO WILL DO

1. Did Jack Nicklaus ever win the Vardon Trophy (for the year's lowest adjusted scoring average)?
2. Did Sam Snead ever win the U.S. Open?
3. If you're in a bunker, are you allowed to touch sand with your club to determine its condition?
4. Did Chi Chi Rodriguez ever win a major in his PGA career?
5. Is it true that Ben Hogan was born in Dublin, Ireland?

ANSWERS

1. No.
2. No.
3. No- It's a two-stroke penalty.
4. No.
5. No- Hogan was born in Dublin, Texas.

CHIP SHOT

"Be funny on the golf course? Do I kid my best friend's mother about her heart condition?"

-*Phil Silvers*

FRIED EGGS AND UNPLAYABLE LIES

If these golfers didn't have bad luck, they wouldn't have any luck at all. Can you name them?

1. He was disqualified from the 1980 U.S. Open after a traffic tie-up caused him to miss his tee time.
2. These two golfers can say that they've lost all four majors in playoffs.
3. In 1986, he was disqualified from both the Phoenix Open and the L.A. Open for hitting someone else's ball.
4. His unfortunate legacy will be as the man who signed an incorrect scored at the 1968 Masters.
5. He has the dubious distinction of playing The Masters the most times without winning it.

ANSWERS

1. Seve Ballesteros.
2. Greg Norman and Craig Wood.
3. Wayne Grady.
4. Roberto DeVicenzo, who lost to Bob Goalby.
5. Gene Littler entered 26 Masters between 1954 and 1980, winning none.

GOING OUT

Name the golf courses described below.

1. At 107 yards, its 7th hole is the shortest in the history of the majors.
2. The course where the United States lost the Ryder Cup for the first time on American soil.
3. Its 17th hole is called the Road Hole.
4. The South Carolina course which was awarded a Ryder Cup before it was completed.
5. The first clubhouse in America opened here in 1892.

ANSWERS

1. Pebble Beach.
2. Muirfield Village in Dublin, Ohio.
3. The Old Course at St. Andrews.
4. The Ocean Course at Kiawah Island.
5. Shinnecock Hills in South Hampton, NY.

CHIP SHOT

"Golf isn't a sport, it's men in bad pants walking."

-Rosie O'Donnell

AMATEUR NIGHT

1. What golfer won the U.S. Amateur in 1974 and, two years later, was the U.S. Open champion?
2. Who was the first golfer to repeat as U.S. Junior Amateur champion?
3. Who was the first amateur to win the U.S. Open?
4. If a Walker Cup is tied, which team (United States or Great Britain and Ireland) keeps the cup?
5. These two University teammates finished tied for the individual championship in 1972. Any guesses?

ANSWERS

1. Jerry Pate.
2. Tiger Woods won the event in 1991, 1992 and 1993.
3. Francis Ouimet won the Open in 1913.
4. In the event of a tie, the Cup is retained for another two years by the previous winner.
5. Ben Crenshaw and Tom Kite.

INITIALLY SPEAKING

Identify each golfer from the initials and clues.

1. T.K.- Won the 1992 U.S. Open at the age of 42.
2. M.B.- Dubbed "Mr. X" for his fondness of solitude.
3. K.W.- Came from eight strokes back to win the 1999 duMaurier Classic, her first major.
4. P.T.- Five time winner of the British Open.
5. M.W.- At the age of fourteen, this female phenom shot rounds of 72 and 68 for a 140 in the PGA Tour Sony Open to miss the cut by just one shot.

ANSWERS

1. Tom Kite.
2. Miller Barber.
3. Karrie Webb.
4. Peter Thomson.
5. Michelle Wie.

CHIP SHOT

"Golf is great exercise, particularly climbing
in and out of the carts."

-Jack Benny

THE OVER THE HILL CLUB

Below is a list of golfers, all of whom won their first titles after their 35th birthday. You job is to match them up with the event.

Golfer, age		Event
1. Jerry Barber, 45	a)	1996 British Open
2. Roberto DeVicenzo, 44	b)	1960 PGA Championship
3. Jay Hebert, 37	c)	1967 British Open
4. Don January, 37	d)	1961 PGA Championship
5. Tom Lehman, 37	e)	1967 PGA Championship

ANSWERS

1. d
2. c
3. b
4. e
5. a

CHIP SHOT

"Retire to what. I'm a golfer and a fisherman.
I've got nothing to retire to."

-Julius Boros

SCRAMBLE

Listed below are U.S. Amateur champions who went on to successful careers on the PGA Tour. Unscramble their names for the answers.

1. STUIJN NRLEADO
2. NAYNL KDINWSA
3. TCSOT PNKALRVE
4. IRCAG DARLEST
5. HLIP KLESICONM

ANSWERS

1. Justin Leonard.
2. Lanny Wadkins.
3. Scott Verplank.
4. Craig Stadler.
5. Phil Mickelson.

CHIP SHOT

"I learn English from American pros –
that's why I speak so bad. I call it P.G.A. English."

-Roberto de Vicenzo

PLAYING BY THE RULES

1. The caddy lost my putter. Can I replace it during the round?
2. Can I remove an anthill from the green?
3. My ball just rolled out of sight down a drainpipe. What do I do?
4. My ball is next to a tree. Can I hit left-handed with a right-handed club?
5. Can I use a little billiards chalk on my 7-iron?

ANSWERS

1. No.
2. Yes.
3. Place a new ball closest to spot where the original ball entered the drainpipe.
4. Yes (as long as it doesn't improve my lie).
5. No.

LINKS LUNACY

1. In 1954, Laddie Lukas shot an 87 at the Sandy Lodge Golf Course in England, a decent performance, but considering what Lukas wearing, it was extraordinary. Have any idea what it was?

2. Several decades ago, a Tournament of Champions was held in Las Vegas. Bet you can't guess the denomination of the prize money.

3. One of the nuttiest golf tournaments ever was the Hawaiian Holiday Masters in Honokaa, Hawaii. What did they use in place of golf balls?

4. The Bionic Invitation is held in Aiken, South Carolina. Can you specify the requirements in order to qualify?

5. In Kansas City, Missouri, there's a tournament call the Jim Smith Open. Who is it open to?

ANSWERS

1. A blindfold.
2. Silver dollars.
3. Macadamia nuts.
4. You must have had a joint surgically replaced.
5. Anyone named Jim Smith, of course. And yes, the trophy is engraved before the tournament.

SCREEN TEST

1. Dino Crocetti and Joseph Levitch starred in the farcical film *The Caddy*. You know them better by their stage names. What are they?

2. Here's another "aka." An eighteen-minute, black and white short, titled *The Golf Specialist* (1930), featured William Claude Dukenfield making his first film. Who is he?

3. Susan Clark portrayed Babe Didrikson Zaharias in the 1975 television movie about her. What was its title?

4. Sean Connery stars in this film where he plays golf against his nemesis, a game in which his opponent's caddy has a hat rim that can decapitate stone statues. What's the name of the film?

5. What was the original name of the AT&T Pebble Beach National Pro-Am? (Big hint: It was named after a favorite of Santa's as this film star/singer recorded *White Christmas*.)

ANSWERS

1. Dean Martin and Jerry Lewis.
2. W.C. Fields.
3. *Babe*.
4. *Goldfinger*.
5. The Bing Crosby Professional-Amateur.

CHIP SHOT

"Some worship in churches, some in synagogues, some on golf courses."

-Adlai Stevenson

WHO AM I?

1. I was the first player to break 60 on the PGA Tour.
2. Doug Weaver, Mark Wiebe, Jerry Pate and I all recorded aces on the 6th hole at the 1989 U.S. Open.
3. My putter's nickname was Calamity Jane.
4. I own the record for the most consecutive PGA Tour victories, 11.
5. On April 13, 1986, I became the oldest player to win the Masters.

ANSWERS

1. Al Geiberger, in 1977.
2. Nick Price.
3. Bobby Jones.
4. Byron Nelson, in 1945.
5. Jack Nicklaus, who was 46 at the time.

CHIP SHOT

"Golf is a game in which the slowest people are
in front of you, and the fastest are behind you."

-Mark Price

THE MATCH GAME

Link the player to the nickname.

1.	Corey Pavin	a) The Grip
2.	Isao Aoki	b) The Squire
3.	Ed Fiori	c) Tower
4.	Craig Parry	d) The Bulldog
5.	Gene Sarazen	e) Popeye

ANSWERS

1. d
2. c
3. a
4. e
5. b

CHIP SHOT

"Golf is good for the soul. You get so mad at yourself,
you forget to hate your enemies."

-Will Rogers

COMMON LINKS

Identify the common term, used in a different way,
that each sport listed below has with the game of golf.
The first letter has been provided for you and Santa
has completed number one as an example.

1. Badminton .... B irdie
2. Baseball.............................. P_____
3. Tennis .... A_____
4. Boxing............................... D_____
5. Football .... F_____
6. Auto Racing .... D_____

ANSWERS

1. Birdie.
2. Pitch.
3. Ace.
4. Draw.
5. Field.
6. Driver.

CHIP SHOT

"Nothing increases a golf score like witnesses."

-Ken Colameo

JACK OF CLUBS

1. True or false? Jack Nicklaus was the first modern-day professional to win all the majors at least twice.
2. Where did Jack Nicklaus attend college?
3. Nicklaus was the first to win back-to-back Masters titles … In what years?
4. He's won the most majors. How many?
5. At the 2005 British Open, he made an emotional departure from competition, and he did it his way with a birdie putt on the 18th hole. Can you name the fellow golfer who said about Nicklaus, "Words are not enough. They should make him out of gold and stick a little Jack on every tee box?"
   a) Tiger Woods b) Nick Faldo c) Tom Watson or d) Mr. Watson

ANSWERS

1. True.
2. Ohio State.
3. 1965 and '66.
4. 18.
5. B … And speaking of letter "A," Woods said,
   "He is the greatest champion that's ever lived."

CHIP SHOT

"I own the erasers for all the miniature golf pencils."

-*Steven Wright*

WORDPLAY

See if you can identify the golf term from the
high falootin' description given below.

1. Aerodynamic Feathered Flyer.
2. Humphrey Bogart deuced.
3. Avocado, Chartreuse, Lime, Mint and Kelly.
4. Concavity covered sphere
5. Hydrogen Dioxide Danger.
6. Cross-Sectional Julienne.
7. Silicone Dioxide Danger.
8. Haliaeetus Leucocephalus.
9. A Limb of the Vertebrate Family Canidae.
10. Uniform Resource Locators of Hypertext Markup Language.

ANSWERS

1. Birdie.
2. Double Bogey.
3. Greens.
4. Golf ball.
5. Water hazard.
6. Slice.
7. Sand trap.
8. Eagle.
9. Dogleg.
10. Links.

WHO SAID IT?

1. "I went to play golf and I tried to shoot my age, but shot my weight instead."
   a) Bob Hope b) David Letterman c) Kenny Rogers d) Mr. Rogers
2. "Golf is one of the few sports where a white man can dress like a black pimp."
   a) George Carlin b) Dave Barry c) Robin Williams d) Venus Williams
3. "The world's coming to an end. The world's best golfer is black and the world's best rapper is white."
   a) Chris Rock b) Sinbad c) Dennis Miller d) Mitch Miller
4. "I enjoy the 'oohs' and 'aahs' from the gallery when I hit my drives, but I'm pretty tired of the 'aaws' and 'uhhs' when I miss the putts."
   a) Miller Barber b) John Daly c) Jack Nicklaus d) St. Nicholas
5. "Golf is the most fun you can have without taking your clothes off."
   a) Chi Chi Rodriguez b) Groucho Marx c) Jackie Mason
   d) Perry Mason

ANSWERS

1. a
2. c
3. a
4. b
5. a

CHIP SHOT

"Never wash your ball on the tee of a water hazard."

-Bill Montooth

FOUR-LETTER MEN

The answers to these clues are all four-letter last names.

1. He burst onto the golf scene in fairy-tale fashion with a win in the 1991 PGA Championship.
2. He was known as "Champagne Tony."
3. This golfer chipped in from 35 years on the second sudden-death hole of the 1987 Masters to seize victory from Greg Norman.
4. Many U.S. presidents have been golfing enthusiasts, but do you know who was the first?
5. In 1988, he became the first golfer from Great Britain to win the Masters.

ANSWERS

1. John Daly.
2. Tony Lema.
3. Larry Mize.
4. William Howard Taft.
5. Scotsman Sandy Lyle.

CHIP SHOT

"I may be the only golfer never to have broken a single putter – if you don't count the one I twisted and threw into a bush."

-Thomas Boswell

LAUGH-IN TIME-OUT

...Time for another trivia break
before we head for the nineteenth hole.

1. Who was the top golfer in North Africa?
2. Why is golf a lot like taxes?
3. What did the Siamese twin golfers name their book?
4. What's the easiest golf stroke?
5. What did they the pub for vulgar golfers?

ANSWERS

1. Gene Sarahazen.
2. You drive very hard to get to the green only to wind up in a hole.
3. Tee for Two.
4. The fourth putt.
5. Par For The Coarse.

LINGO OF THE LINKS

1. What is an albatross?
2. What's the modern-day name for the mashie?
3. What's the difference between match play and medal play?
4. What does the phrase "through the green" mean?
5. You're my caddy as I play the back nine of the British Open.
   I ask for my jigger. What club did you hand me?

ANSWERS

1. It's the British term for a double-eagle.
2. The 5-iron.
3. The winner at match play is determined by the total holes won, while medal play is by total strokes.
4. It means the entire golf course except the teeing ground, the putting green and all hazards. Out-of-bounds, of course, is not considered to be part of the course.
5. The 4-iron.

MISCELLANEOUS MINDBENDERS

1. Name the golfer who has the most professional titles in history.
2. What is four-ball?
3. What "record" did Fred Funk achieve at the Ryder Cup in 2004?
4. What course is nicknamed "Hogan's Alley?"
5. True or false? The golfer who finishes first on the PGA Tour official money list is given the Jack Nicklaus Award.

ANSWERS

1. Kathy Whitworth, 88.
2. It's a round of golf where two players are paired against two others. Each player plays their ball through a hole, but only the best score of the two is chalked up on the scorecard.
3. At the age of 48, he was the oldest golfer to win a berth at the tournament.
4. The Colonial Country Club in Fort Worth, Texas. A native Texan, Ben Hogan won five tournaments there.
5. False ... It's the Arnold Palmer Award.

TIGER'S BRITISH TIDBITS

1. Tiger Woods cruised to the British Open victory this year. In all, that marked how many majors that he's won?
2. He won the tournament by five shots, the largest margin in any major since someone won it at St. Andrews by eight five years ago. Who was that?
3. Who finished second at the 2005 event?
4. A year earlier, Tiger finished ninth at the British Open. Who was the winner?
5. If Tiger were to succeed in surpassing the record for most wins at the British Open, just how many wins would he need?

ANSWERS

1. 10.
2. Tiger, himself.
3. Colin Montgomerie.
4. Todd Hamilton.
5. Seven … The current record is held by Harry Vardon with 6.

CHIP SHOT

"Golf is a way of testing ourselves while enjoying ourselves."

-Arnold Palmer

DUFFER'S DILEMMA

You decide which of the golfers is the correct answer.

1. He was the first golfer to win PGA Tour titles in four different decades. Was it Sam Snead or Arnold Palmer?
2. She won the most major championships in LPGA Tour history. Was it Patty Berg or Pat Bradley?
3. He was the first golfer to use a female caddy while playing in the Masters. Was it George Archer or Nick Faldo?
4. He was the first South African golfer to win the British Open. Was it Ernie Els or Bobby Locke?
5. He had 17 wins on the PGA Tour before reaching his 30th birthday. Was it Lee Trevino or Johnny Miller?

ANSWERS

1. Sam Snead.
2. Patty Berg … She won 16 majors in her career.
3. George Archer's daughter caddied for him in the 1983 tournament.
4. Bobby Locke first won in 1949.
   He also won it in 1950, '52 and '57.
5. Johnny Miller.

CHIP SHOT

"Don't play too much golf. Two rounds a day are plenty."

-Harry Vardon

PUTTER POTPOURRI

1. What LPGA player receives the Vare Trophy at the end of the year?

2. True or false? Golfers have to be at least 50 years old to play in the U.S. Senior Open, but 55 years old to enter the U.S. Senior Amateur.

3. In the nineteenth century, most golf shafts were made of what type of wood?

4. Of all the players to ever win a major title, who comes first alphabetically?

5. Which state has the most golf courses?

ANSWERS

1. It's awarded to the player with the lowest scoring average for the year.
2. True.
3. Hickory.
4. Tommy Aaron, who won the 1973 Masters.
5. Florida, with California a close second.

SCHOOL DAYS

Match the golfer with the school attended.

1. John Cook
2. Justin Leonard
3. Tom Lehman
4. Hale Irwin
5. Fred Couples
6. Raymond Floyd
7. Phil Mickelson
8. Corey Pavin
9. John Daly
10. Tom Watson

a) Arizona State
b) Houston
c) UCLA
d) Ohio State
e) Arkansas
f) Colorado
g) Minnesota
h) Stanford
i) Texas
j) North Carolina

ANSWERS

1. d
2. i
3. g
4. f
5. b
6. j
7. a
8. c
9. e
10. h

OF COURSE

Name the golf courses described below.

1. It's where Bobby Jones capped off his Grand Slam with a win in the U.S. Amateur.
2. The Cherry Hills Country Club has hosted the U.S. Open more than once. Where is it located?
3. Which golf club is acknowledged to be the oldest in the world?
4. It's 17th hole is called the Road Hole.
5. Here's a gift from Santa- The Masters is played here.

ANSWERS

1. Merion Country Club.
2. Englewood, Colorado.
3. Honourable Company of Edinburgh Golfers in Muirfield, Scotland. They are descendants of the Gentlemen Golfers which was recognized by the Edinburgh Town council in 1744 (ten years before St. Andrews).
4. The Old Course at St. Andrews.
5. Augusta National.

MISSING LINKS

Which one doesn't belong, and why?

1. Jack Nicklaus, Arnold Palmer, Tiger Woods, Lee Trevino.
2. Jerry Heard, Lee Trevino, Bobby Nichols, Corey Pavin.
3. Chip Beck, Al Geiberger, Shigeka Maruyama, David Duval.
4. Lou Graham, David Graham, Tom Watson, Andy North.
5. Jack Nicklaus, Billy Casper, Johnny Miller, Hubert Green.

ANSWERS

1. Lee Trevino – He never won The Masters.
2. Corey Pavin – He's never been, knock on wood, struck by lightning.
3. Shigeki Maruyama – He shot a 58 in the first round of qualifying for the 2000 U.S. Open. The others have recorded 59s on the PGA Tour.
4. Andy North – The others have won one U.S. Open. North won two of them.
5. Jack Nicklaus – He never won three straight PGA tour events like the others.

LADIES' CHOICE

1. She was the winner of the 2005 LPGA Championship.
2. Six LPGA Tour Hall of Famers (or Hall of Fame members-to-be) have accomplished the Career Grand Slam, winning each of the designated majors during their playing careers. How many can you name?
3. Mickey Wright was the first golfer to defend her U.S. Women's Open title. Who was second?
4. Who was the 2005 U.S. Women's Open winner?
5. Her hole-in-one in the 1959 U.S. Women's Open made her the first woman to record an ace in USGA competion. Do you know who it is?

ANSWERS

1. Annika Sorenstam.
2. Pat Bradley (1986), Juli Inkster (1999),
   Annika Sorenstam (2003), Louise Suggs (1957),
   Karrie Webb (2001) and Mickey Wright (1962).
3. Donna Caponi won the title in 1969 and '70.
4. Birdie Kim.
5. Patty Berg.

CHIP SHOT

"The woods are full of long drivers."

-Harvey Penick

GOLF GEOGRAPHY

1. Excluding the British Isles, what country had the first golf course?
2. Name the native country of Vijay Singh.
3. Name the golf club that hosted the first U.S. Open in 1895.
4. Where is the Oakland Hills Country Club, site of numerous major championships, located?
5. The Inverness Club was the site of two playoff losses by Greg Norman in the PGA Championship. Where's it located?

ANSWERS

1. India – The Royal Calcutta Golf Club was established in 1829.
2. Fiji.
3. The Newport (Rhode Island) Golf Club.
4. Birmingham, Michigan.
5. Toledo, Ohio.

CHIP SHOT

"The only shot you can be dead sure of
are those you've had already."

-Byron Nelson

BY THE NUMBERS

Do you know...

1. The diameter of a golf ball?
2. The diameter of a golf hole?
3. The most common 18-hole par on golf courses around the world?
4. The number of clubs allowed in tournament competition?
5. Tiger Woods' record-setting non-adjusted scoring average in 2000 ?

ANSWERS

1. 1.68 inches
2. 4.25 inches
3. 72
4. Fourteen
5. 68.17

CHIP SHOT

"The most exquisitely satisfying act in the world is that of throwing a club. The full backswing, the delayed wrist action, the flowing follow-through, followed by that unique whirring sound, reminiscent only of a passing flock of starlings, is without parallel in sport."

-Henry Longhurst

FACT OR FIB?

1. No golfer named Joe won a major championship in the 1900s.
2. No Irishman has ever won a major championship.
3. President Grover Cleveland decided against taking up golf because he was too fat.
4. In 1994, Fuzzy Zoeller earned more than one million dollars, but didn't win a tournament.
5. Gene Sarazen invented the sand wedge.

ANSWERS

1. Fact.
2. Fib- Ireland's Fred Daly won the 1947 British Open by one stroke.
3. Fact.
4. Fact.
5. Fact.

CHIP SHOT

"You've just one problem. You stand too close to the ball – after you've hit it."

-Sam Snead, to a pupil

A MATTER OF SECONDS

1. Who finished second at the 2005 British Open?
2. Birdie Kim was the surprising winner of the 2005 U.S. Women's Open conducted by the USGA. Can you name one of the two golfers who finished second?
3. Patty Berg is the all-time LPGA majors leader with 16 titles. Can you name either of the two women who are second, each with 13 majors wins?
4. Jack Nicklaus won three PGA Championships in the '70s. Who was runner-up with two?
5. Hale Irwin won three consecutive PGA Seniors' Championships in the '90s. What senior golfer won two during that decade?

ANSWERS

1. Colin Montgomerie.
2. Morgan Pressel and Brittany Lang.
3. Mickey Wright and Louise Suggs.
4. Dave Stockton.
5. Lee Trevino.

CHIP SHOT

"Want a foolproof way to knock at least six strokes off of your score – skip the last hole."

-Leslie Nielsen

GIVE ME A VOWEL

All of the vowels have been removed from the following quotes.
Otherwise, everything's intact. See if you reconstruct them.

1. " played Cvl Wr glf. wnt t n 61 nd cm bck n 65."
   —*Henny Youngman*

2. "Nnty prcnt f th ptts tht fll shrt dn't g n."-*Yogi Berra*

3. "Glf s gm n whch y yll fr, sht sx, nd wrt dwn fv ."
   —*Paul Harvey*

4. "Thy cll t glf bcs ll th thr fr-lttr wrds wr tkn."
   —*Raymond Floyd*

5. " hv tp whch cn tk fv strks ff nyn 's glf gm .
   t's clld n rsr." —*Arnold Palmer*

ANSWERS

1. "I played Civil War golf. I went out in 61 and came back in 65."
2. "Ninety percent of the putts that fall short don't go in."
3. "Golf is a game in which you yell fore, shoot six, and write down five."
4. "They call it golf because all the other four-letter words were taken."
5. "I have a tip which can take five strokes off anyone's golf game. It's called an eraser."

PUTTER POTPOURRI- Take 2

1. Legal or illegal? My ball accidentally hits my golf cart.
2. This famous seaside course with its feared 107-yard, par-3 7th hole was designed by amateur golfer Jack Neville in 1919. Name it.
3. Do you know what club astronaut Alan Shepard used for his "moon" shot in 1971?
4. His middle name was Tyre. Do you know the full name of this amateur great?
5. *A Feel for the Game* was a New York Times bestseller written by what golfer?

ANSWERS

1. Illegal. It's a two-stroke penalty.
2. Pebble Beach Golf Links in California.
3. A 6-iron.
4. Robert Tyre Jones, Jr.
5. Ben Crenshaw.

CHIP SHOT

"To miss a tree, aim straight at it."

-Tom Colver

'TIS THE SEASON

Santa's left a message for you. Simply follow the instructions below to find out what it is.

1. If a pitching wedge was once called a jigger, remove all the h's.
2. If Curtis Strange has a twin brother, remove all the t's.
3. If Arnold Palmer was the first golfer to be named Sports Illustrated's Sportsman of the Year, remove all the e's.
4. If Byron Nelson had more PGA Tour wins than Ben Hogan, remove all the a's.
5. If golf Hall of Famer Nancy Lopez is married to a World Series MVP, remove all the n's.

The message: THANPEPY HEOLTINDATYS!

ANSWERS

1. It's not ... It was formerly called a spade mashie.
2. He does ... His brother's named Allen.
3. He was, in 60.
4. He didn't ... Hogan had 64 wins, Nelson, 52.
5. She is – Ray Knight, the 1986 Series MVP, of the New York Mets.

The message: HAPPY HOLIDAYS!
(And have an extra-special Merry Christmas!)